INSIDE...

D0264865

CRIMINAL CONNECTIONS!

The list below reveals all of the villains that criminal mastermind, the Kingpin wants to recruit into his gang. See how many you can find in the word grid opposite!

BIGMAN
HAMMERHEAD
TOMBSTONE
SILVERMANE
FANCYDAN
BLACKWING
THE OX
VULTURE

U	E	H	S	T	E	R	I	O	P	G
E	N	A	M	R	E	V	L	I	S	D
U	O	M	D	P	T	O	H	L	W	T
L	T	M	R	R	R	Y	C	K	E	H
A	S	E	D	O	D	M	E	N	G	E
H	B	R	O	R	W	Y	M	L	A	O
B	M	H	O	N	A	M	G	I	B	X
Y	O	E	M	V	U	L	T	U	R	E
E	T	A	A	R	L	E	T	W	A	A
N	A	D	Y	C	N	A	F	H	C	L
R	R	R	B	L	A	C	K	W	I	N	G

PICTURE IMPERFECT!

Spidey's belt camera was damaged during the fight with the Kingpin, ruining his latest snaps. Take a look at the pictures below and see if you can work out who is in each!

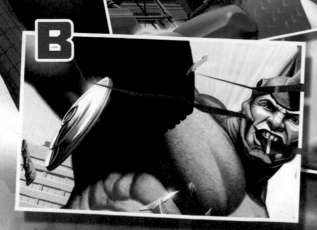

A

B

C

D

Answers: Picture Imperfect- A=Captain America, B=Rhino, C=Silver Surfer, D=Sandman.

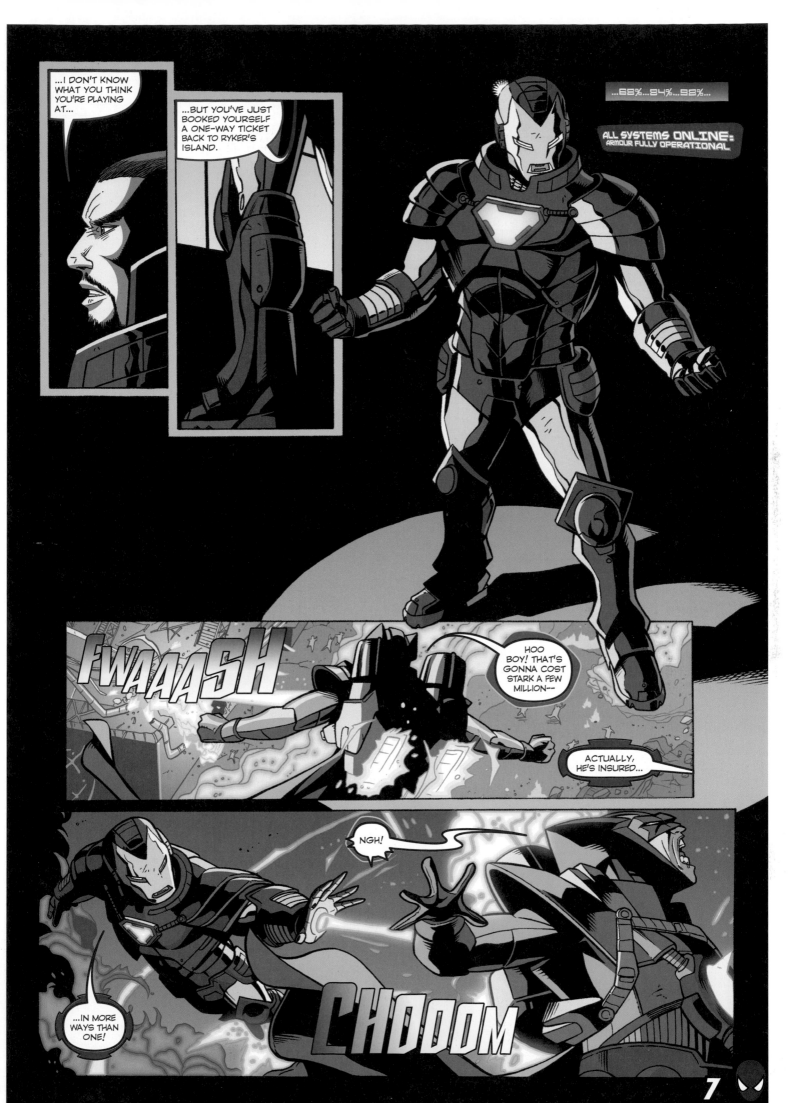

EXCELLENT. AND NOW THAT'S DEALT WITH, LET'S RETURN TO THE REAL AGENDA...

"...WHICH IS SHUTTING DOWN THIS FACILITY..."

KABOOM!

"...WITH TACTICAL STRIKES ON EACH OF ITS KEY INSTALLATIONS."

FWAAASH

OUTSTANDING, BOSS...THE PLACE IS LOOKING LIKE A WAR ZONE.

PRECISELY, THERE MUST BE BILLIONS WORTH OF DAMAGE -- ALL CAUSED BY ITS SO-CALLED PROTECTOR.

BUT TO COMPLETELY DESTROY STARK INTERNATIONAL, WE NEED TO DEAL WITH THE OTHER SITES.

ON ME, MELTER, WE'VE GOT WORK TO DO. OR RATHER, IRON MAN HAS.

14

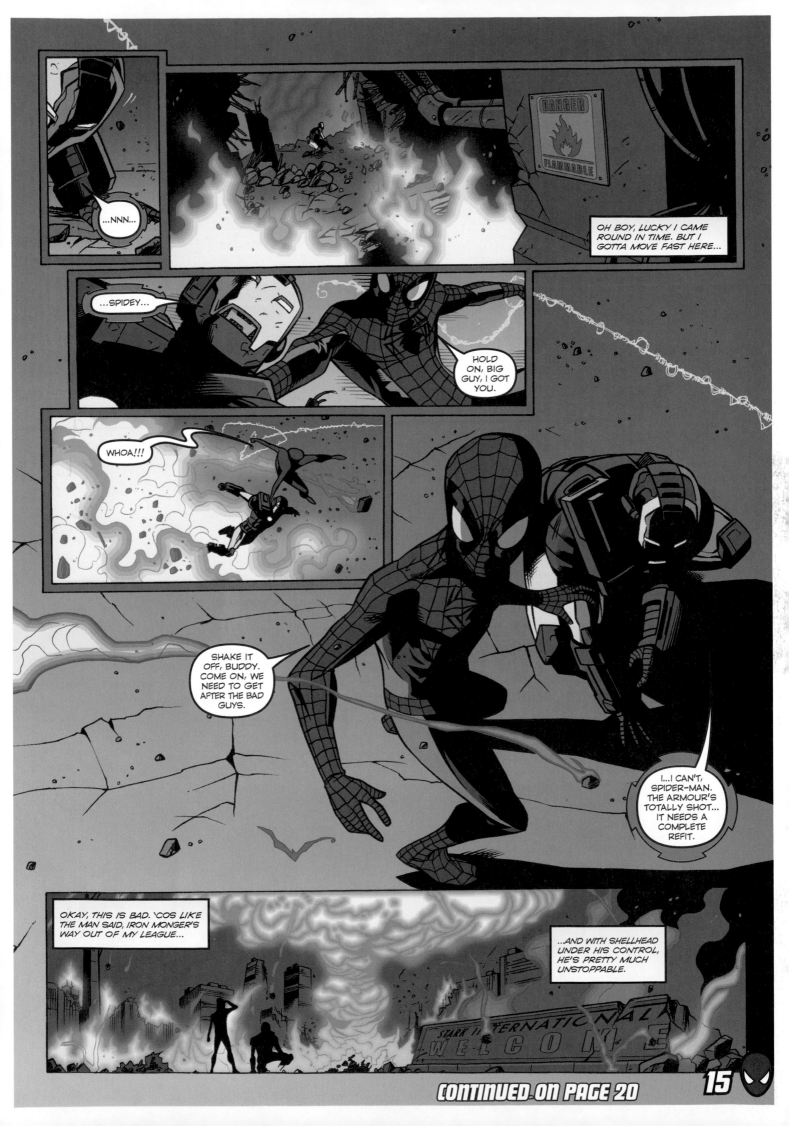

CONTINUED ON PAGE 20

CRACK THE CODE!

Spidey needs to try and stop the computer hacking device on Iron Man!

SEARCHING... POSSIBLE 5-DIGIT PASSWORD CODE...

Use the clues from Iron Man's CPU to work out the password combination!

$$15 - 7 = 8$$
$$2 \times 3 = 6$$
$$5 + 4 = 9$$
$$6 - 5 = 1$$
$$4 \times 2 = 8$$

HAVING A BLAST!

Oh no, the code didn't work! Iron Man's down and out, so Spidey has to get to War Machine for help!

A
B
C
D

Can you find the route along War Machine's trail that avoids the energy blasts?

CENTRAL!

SMOKE SCREEN!

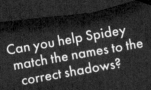

Can you help Spidey match the names to the correct shadows?

IRON MONGER   WAR MACHINE   MELTER   IRON MAN

A B C D

TARGET PRACTICE!

Can you help target the weak spots on Iron Monger's battle suit?

Hold a pencil above the picture, and drop it five times. See if you can hit all of the targets!

CAPTURED

Wealthy industrialist Tony Stark was on a field test for one of his latest inventions, when he was attacked and captured.

DEADLY DEAL

Hit in the chest by a piece of metal that would kill him within a matter of weeks, his captors agreed to save him, but only if he built them a powerful weapon!

FREEDOM FIGHTER

They got more than they bargained for though, as Stark built an experimental battle suit that allowed him to fight his way free!

I AM IRON MAN

Back in America, Stark adapted the suit, and used it to battle bad guys as the invincible Iron man!

Iron man

Jet pack

Strength-enhancing armour

ULTIMATE UPGRADES

Stark is constantly rebuilding his armour with new weapons and modifications – here are some of our favourites!

Pulse beams

Multifunctional uni-beam

Repulsor rays

IT TAKES A LOT OF FIRE POWER TO TAKE DOWN IRON MONGER. LUCKILY, THESE GUYS HAVE IT!

SPIDER FILE:

GREAT ESCAPE

When airforce pilot James Rhodes helped Tony Stark escape from an Asian jungle, the two became good friends.

IRON DEPUTY

So good, that when Stark had to give up being Iron Man for a while, Rhodes was the only man he trusted enough to take his place.

BATTLE SUIT

When Stark was ready to return as Iron Man, he built Rhodes his own battle suit. Bursting with weapons, it was nicknamed War Machine!

WAR MACHINE

TOOLED UP

With a name like War Machine, you'd expect this armoured suit to have more weapons than you can shake a repulsor ray at... and you'd be right!

Rocket launchers

Gatling gun

Repulsor rays

Jet boots

Chest uni-beam

Energy cannons

IRON MONGER...

YES, I SEE HIM. BUT DON'T FRET, EVERYTHING'S UNDER CONTROL.

CYBERNETIC INTERFACE: TRANSMITTING...

VOOOMPH

PHEW! AND OKAY, THE BOOTS HELPED... BUT I COULDN'T HAVE DONE IT WITHOUT THE OL' SPIDER-REFLEXES.

VOOOMPH

CAREFUL, SPIDEY. DON'T GET TOO OVERCONFIDENT.

OVERCONFIDENT? MOI?

KA BOOM!

OKAY, I'M GOOD. BUT SHELLHEAD'S REACTIONS ARE A LITTLE OFF TOO, ON ACCOUNT OF BEING REMOTE CONTROLLED...

23

...AND NEXT MORNING, I'M BACK AT THE LONG ISLAND SITE, TO TAKE CARE OF THE LOOSE ENDS.

MISTER STARK, OVER HERE.

PETER! WE'VE BEEN WORRIED SICK, IN CASE YOU WERE LYING HURT SOMEWHERE...OR WORSE!

SORRY, MISTER STARK. BUT I GOT SEPARATED FROM THE OTHERS ON THE WAY TO THE SAFE ROOM LAST NIGHT...

...AND WHEN I ENDED UP OUTSIDE, THERE WAS ALL THIS FIGHTING. SO I GUESS I PANICKED AND RAN.

I COULDN'T BLAME YOU, YOUNG MAN. BUT WHAT HAPPENED TO YOUR FACE?

OH, THAT? I, ER...GOT HIT BY A BIT OF DEBRIS. BUT IT'S FINE, REALLY.

NO, IT'S NOT. IT HAPPENED ON MY PREMISES, AND YOU DESERVE COMPENSATION.

MISS POTTS, I WANT A MONTH'S WAGES PAID INTO MISTER PARKER'S ACCOUNT. THAT'S INDUSTRY RATES, NOT INTERN'S.

I'LL GET ON IT RIGHT AWAY, MISTER STARK.

OKAY, FEELING GUILTY FOR LYING NOW. BUT I COULDN'T EXACTLY TELL HIM WHAT REALLY HAPPENED.

BESIDES, I SUPPOSE I DID HELP SAVE THE CORPORATION BILLIONS LAST NIGHT...

...AND AUNT MAY DOES NEED A NEW WASHING MACHINE. PLUS THERE'S MY OVERDRAFT, AND MY CREDIT CARD BILLS...

THE END.

SPIDEY

Spidey only has five minutes to reach the other Stark building before it's too late!

TIME CRISIS!

2:00 1:00 1:00 3:00 1:00 1:00 3:00 1:00 2:00 3:00 1:00

STARK

INSTRUCTIONS
1. Each time you pass through a clock, you lose the amount of time shown.
2. Find a route to the Stark building that takes five minutes or less.

STARK INTERNATIONAL
WELCOME

CENTRAL!

QUICK FIX!

Spidey needs to assemble the computer hacking gadget War Machine gave him!

Can you help him by writing the correct letters in each space?

A B C D E

RESCUE MISSION!

Iron Man's back under Iron Monger's control, and destroying buildings!

One of the buildings still has someone in it! Can you work out which one, so Spidey can save them?

ANSWER

A

B

C

SPIDER FILE

IRON MONGER'S NOT THE ONLY VILLAIN OUT THERE WITH A SUPED-UP BATTLE SUIT... TAKE A LOOK AT THESE GUYS!

DOCTOR DOOM

If you want a battle suit to help you take over the world, you'd better make it a good one – and that's exactly what Dr Doom did! As well as strength-enhancing, flight and concussive blasts, the armour has an electrified force field that zaps enemies with 30,000-volt blasts!

TITANIUM MAN

Built with the sole purpose of defeating Iron Man, the Titanium Man armour's tough outer shell makes it impossible for conventional weapons to damage. Add some super-powerful energy beams into the mix, and you've got yourself one heck of a battle suit!

STAMINA

Allows full exertion for 24 hours

STASIS BEAM

Completely paralyses enemies

STRENGTH

Can lift up to 75 tons

SCRAMBLER RAY

Disintergrates almost anything

JET BOOTS

Can fly at the speed of sound

ARMOURED ENEMIES!

CRIMSON DYNAMO

This armour has the power to turn whoever wears it into a human dynamo. Controlling all forms of electricity, flying at 110mph, and firing blasts of up to 50,000 volts – yep, this suit will definitely make your hair stand on end!

DURABILITY
Made of high-tech titanium alloy

GAUNTLETS
Fire concussive blasts

DURABILITY
Impervious to bullets and falls

STRENGTH
Can lift up to 2 tons

GAUNTLETS
Blast electricity over 100 feet

STRENGTH
Can lift up to 2 tons

FORCE FIELD
Creates massive electric shock

JET-PACKS
For high-speed flight

OVERRIDE SYSTEM
Controls and disrupts other electrical devices

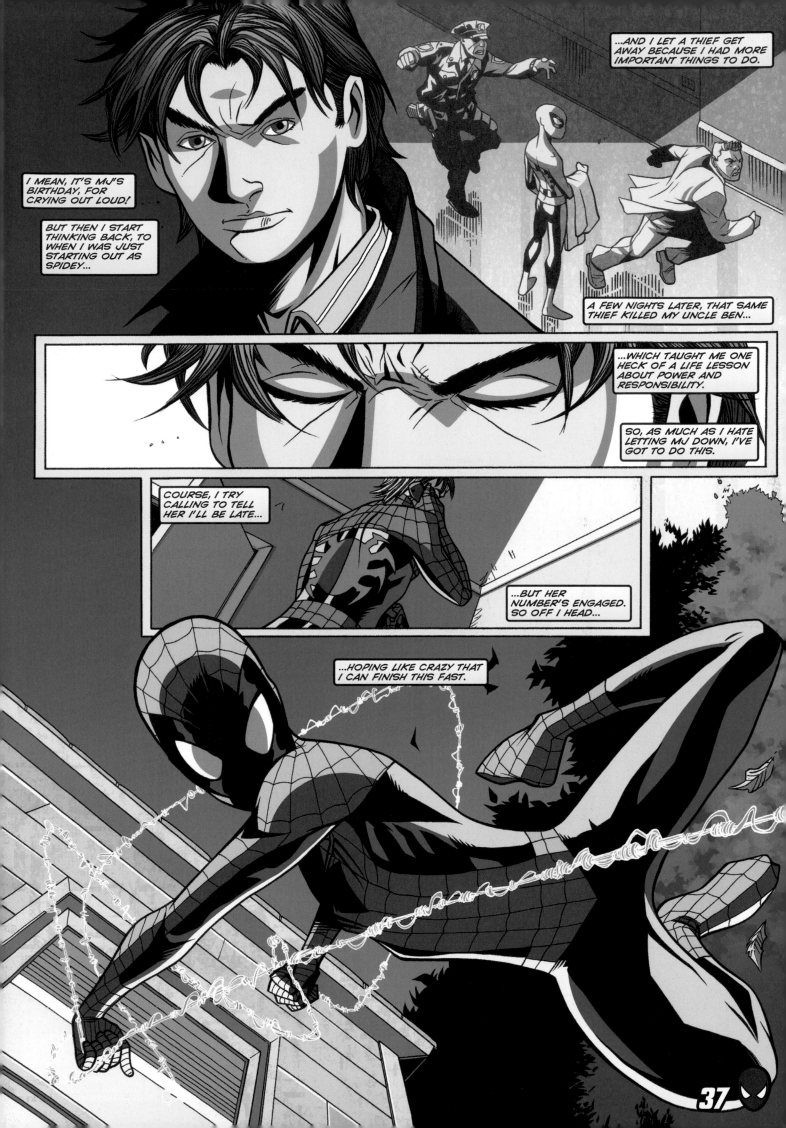

...AND I LET A THIEF GET AWAY BECAUSE I HAD MORE IMPORTANT THINGS TO DO.

I MEAN, IT'S MJ'S BIRTHDAY, FOR CRYING OUT LOUD!

BUT THEN I START THINKING BACK, TO WHEN I WAS JUST STARTING OUT AS SPIDEY...

A FEW NIGHTS LATER, THAT SAME THIEF KILLED MY UNCLE BEN...

...WHICH TAUGHT ME ONE HECK OF A LIFE LESSON ABOUT POWER AND RESPONSIBILITY.

SO, AS MUCH AS I HATE LETTING MJ DOWN, I'VE GOT TO DO THIS.

COURSE, I TRY CALLING TO TELL HER I'LL BE LATE...

...BUT HER NUMBER'S ENGAGED. SO OFF I HEAD...

...HOPING LIKE CRAZY THAT I CAN FINISH THIS FAST.

37

SYMBIOTE SAGA!

WHEN SPIDEY SEPARATED HIMSELF FROM THE PARASITIC SYMBIOTE THAT FORMED HIS BLACK COSTUME, IT WAS THE BIRTH OF THE DEADLIEST ALIEN FAMILY AROUND!

VENOM

Once separated from Spidey, the symbiote slithered away to bond with Spidey-hating journalist Eddie Brock, forming the deadly Venom!

CARNAGE

Eventually, the Venom symbiote 'gave birth' to a spore, which bonded with the psychopathic killer Cletus Kasady to form Carnage!

TOXIN

When Carnage started to spawn, it tried to destroy its offspring, but Venom saved it, allowing it to bond with a policeman and form the tormented crime-fighter, Toxin!

PART ALIEN SYMBIOTE, PART PSYCHOTIC SERIAL KILLER, THEY DON'T COME MUCH DEADLIER THAN CARNAGE, AND HERE'S WHY!

WILD CHILD

Cletus Kasady didn't exactly have a great childhood. After the tragic deaths of his mother and grandmother, his father was sent to prison, warping Cletus' already deranged mind further, and driving him to murder.

BANGED UP

A complete homicidal maniac, Kasady was eventually caught and sent to prison, where he shared a cell with Eddie Brock — the host of the deadly alien Venom symbiote.

IT'S A BOY!

When the symbiote freed Brock from jail, it spawned another life form, which bonded with Kasady, creating Carnage — a being more powerful, merciless and deadly than even Venom!

FEEDING FRENZY

Stopping at nothing to feed his relentless desire to kill, Carnage's only weaknesses are a vulnerability to loud sounds and heat.

CARNAGE ™

TOOLS OF THE TRADE

DISGUISE
Can mimic any type of clothing.

STRENGTH
Stronger than Spider-Man and Venom comined!

WEAPONS
Can fire detachable weapons such as blades and bullets, made from the symbiote!

WEBBING
Produces organic web-like substance to swing from and trap enemies.

PROTECTION
Can easily repel blades and bullets!

HEALING
Can regenerate damaged body tissue at superhuman rates!

SURPRISE
Can deaden Spider-Man's spider-sense for surprise attacks!

SPIDER-FILE:

SECRET WEAPON

Okay, it's not so secret, but their massive tails can deliver a poisonous sting that can kill in seconds.

SKRULLS

This fearsome bunch of shape-shifers travels from galaxy to galaxy, conquering worlds as they go. Luckily the Fantastic Four were around to protect humankind when they set their sights on Earth. Unluckily, the Skrulls responded by creating the Super-Skrull – a warrior blessed with every one of the Fantastic Four's powers!

SECRET WEAPON

Skrulls can morph their bodies into any person or object they can think of. Errr, did that hat stand just move?

SYMBIOTES

Originally brought to Earth from Battleworld by Spidey, these parasites feed off the emotions of their hosts. Since hitching a ride with the webslinger, the symbiotes have gone on to form villains like Venom and Carnage, forcing their hosts to commit more and more vicious acts, and feeding off the adrenaline rush these create.

ALIEN INVA

FROM SYMBIOTES
GET READY FOR AN
OF THE MIGHTIEST
MARVEL

BROOD

Looking like an eight foot tall demonic scorpion, the Brood are hands-down winners of our 'Alien You'd Least Like To Meet Down A Dark Alley' award. And the nastiness doesn't end there – to reproduce, they infect other beings with their embryos, which slowly grow in their host until they're ready to mutate and take over. Yeuch!

SECRET WEAPON

Gladiator's powers depend on his levels of confidence. Without this, he'll turn as weak as a kitten!

...EN ...ION!

...TO SUPER-SKRULL, INTERGALACTIC TOUR ALIENS IN THE UNIVERSE!

SHI'AR

Gladiator, the leader of the Shi'ar's Imperial Guard, is proud, powerful, and one of the meanest fighters in the universe! He boasts of being strong enough to move whole planets, can fly at hyper-speed, project beams as hot as the sun from his eyes, and create gale-force winds with his breath!

MOJO

This big bag of blubber comes from a race called the Spineless Ones, and just loves his television! In fact, he loves it so much, he's started making his own shows, which often involve luring super heroes to his home planet of Mojo World, then filming them as they do battle. And you thought 'Big Brother' was cruel!

SECRET WEAPON

Symbiotes are made more powerful if their host has violent desires too!

SECRET WEAPON

Doctor Strange reckons that Mojo's 'anti-life' force could take out all life on Earth if he ever made it there. Gulp!

51

SPIDEY

ALL TIED UP!

Carnage has got Spidey in a bit of a sticky situation!

Can you help him by working out which symbiote strand he's wrapped up in?

A
B
C

ANSWER

END

MOVING TARGETS!

Now it looks as if Carnage has chucked a few presents our way!

You only have one shot to take each one down. Close your eyes and try to mark each target once with a pencil!

CENTRAL!

DEADLY DISGUISE!

Carnage's symbiote can mimic any kind of clothing,

Can you spot anything that might help Spidey work out which of these guys might be Carnage?

A

B

C

D

E

ANSWER F

WICKED WORDS!

TOTAL 7

How many times can you find the word Carnage in this grid?

Look out for backwards words too!

FOREWARNED IS FOUR ARMED!

...AND SOME BREAKING NEWS JUST IN. IT APPEARS THAT SPIDER-MAN — YES, THAT'S *SPIDER-MAN* — IS ENGAGED IN A CITY-WIDE CRIME SPREE...

WRITER: FERG HANDLEY
PENCILS: JOHN ROYLE
INKS: FAZ CHOUDHURY
COLOURS: GIULIA BRUSCO
LETTERS: PERI GODBOLD

"...AND JUDGING BY THOSE MECHANICAL ARMS HE'S *WEARING*..."

KTASH!

"...IT WOULD APPEAR THAT THE COSTUMED VIGILANTE IS IN LEAGUE WITH HIS OLD ADVERSARY DOCTOR OCTOPUS."

WHUMF

THE APARTMENT OF BLIND LAWYER MATT MURDOCK.

...ATTEMPTS BY POLICE TO HALT THE...

THIS IS CRAZY! BUT IF PETER'S REALLY GONE BAD — AND THAT'S A *BIG* IF — IT'S UP TO *DAREDEVIL* TO STOP HIM.

AND SO...

HEY, YOU WANT TO TELL ME WHAT'S GOING ON, WEBSLINGER?

COME ON, WHATEVER IT IS YOU CAN —

UFFF!

THWAKKK

THIS IS CREEPY, I'VE NEVER *KNOWN* HIM TO BE SO QUIET. WAIT, MY SENSES ARE PICKING UP —

KLANG!

UNGHH!

KRUNCH!

LATER.

FOR THOSE OF YOU JUST JOINING US, SPIDER-MAN'S RAMPAGE SEEMS TO BE OVER. FOLLOWING A BRIEF BATTLE WITH DAREDEVIL, HE ENTERED THE MIDTOWN NATIONAL BANK...

"...EMERGING MINUTES LATER WITH AN UNDISCLOSED SUM IN BANK-NOTES. THEN...

"...AFTER ATTACKING A NEARBY SECURITY VAN, THE ONE-MAN CRIME WAVE DISAPPEARED FROM SIGHT..."

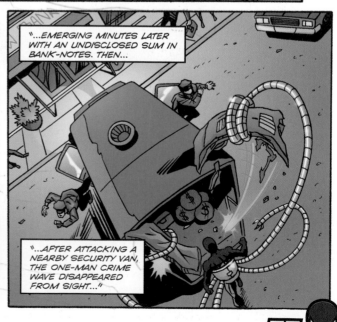

"PARALYSIS WAS TOTAL. AND SO, MENTALLY CONTROLLING MY METAL LIMBS, I SENT MY FOE OUT TO COMMIT HIS CRIMES..."

"...CRIMES THAT WOULD UTTERLY DISCREDIT HIM WHILST I PROFITED FROM THE PROCEEDS. OF COURSE, HIS OBVIOUS IMMOBILITY WOULD HAVE SOON GIVEN THE GAME AWAY..."

"...SO I PROGRAMMED THE HARNESS'S POWER PACK TO ADMINISTER CONSTANT ELECTRICAL SHOCK'S, STIMULATING HIS LIMBS TO MOVEMENT."

"BEST OF ALL, HE WAS CONSCIOUS AT ALL TIMES — FEELING THE PAIN AND COMPLETELY AWARE OF THE OFFENCES HE WAS COMMITTING."

PERHAPS I'LL SEND YOU OUT AGAIN TOMORROW, WALL-CRAWLER. MEANTIME, I THINK I'LL WATCH SOME NEWS...

...AFTER ALL, IT IS RATHER *COMPELLING* VIEWING.

JUST LIKE I FIGURED, IT'S ALL A LOUSY SET-UP. OKAY, FIRST THINGS FIRST...

...LET'S GET SOME OF THIS DOWN YOU.

DAREDEVIL... UHHN...WHAT'RE YOU DOING HERE?

HELPING YOU, BUDDY. SEE, WHILE WE WERE FIGHTING, MY ENHANCED HEARING DETECTED YOUR HEARTBEAT...

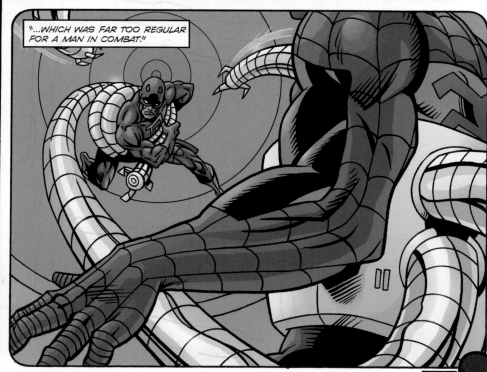

"...WHICH WAS FAR TOO REGULAR FOR A MAN IN COMBAT."

"ALSO, MY HEIGHTENED SENSE OF SMELL IDENTIFIED TRACES OF THAT NERVE AGENT..."

"...JUST BEFORE YOU FLATTENED ME!"

SWOOSH

SO, I HUNTED DOWN AN ANTIDOTE, GOT BACK ON YOUR TRAIL AND FOLLOWED YOU HERE TO OCK'S LITTLE LAIR.

MOST COMMENDABLE, DAREDEVIL. I WONDER IF YOU'LL FEEL SO SMUG...

...WHEN I HAVE CRUSHED THE LIVING BREATH FROM YOUR LUNGS!

NAAAARGH!

LET HIM BE, OCTAVIUS...

THUUUD

...'COS WE GOT BUSINESS.

58

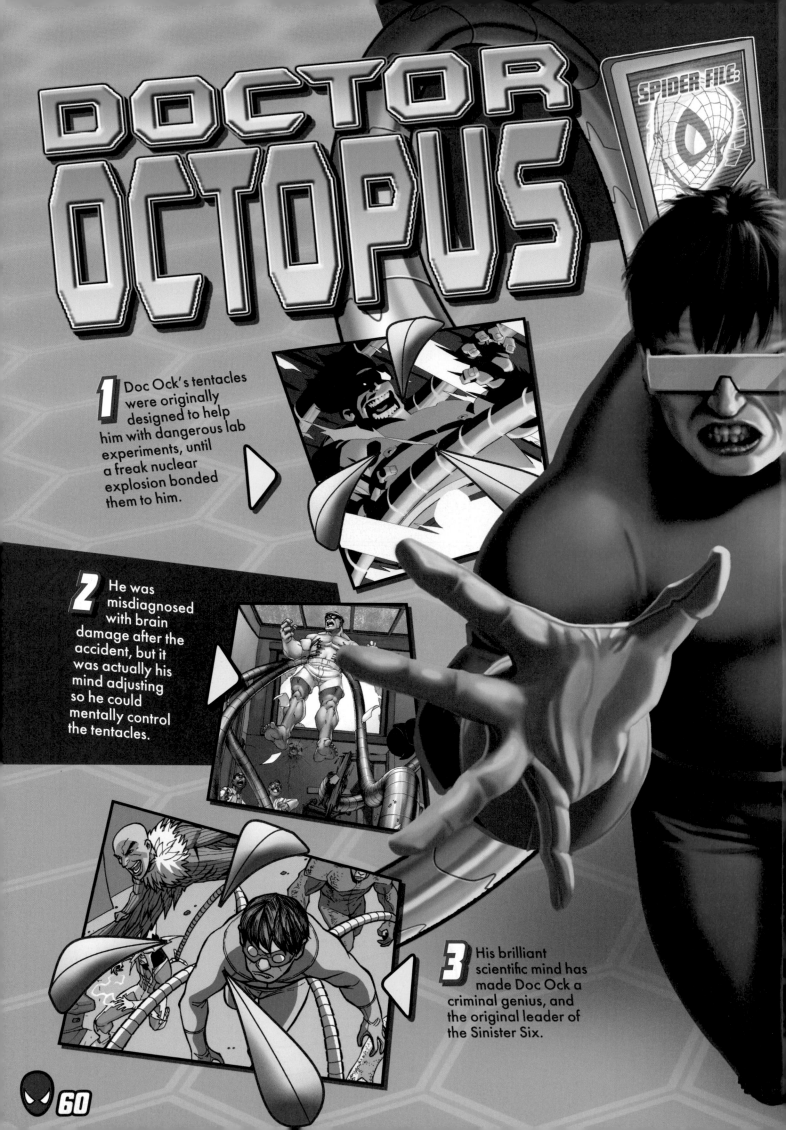

DOCTOR OCTOPUS

SPIDER FILE:

1 Doc Ock's tentacles were originally designed to help him with dangerous lab experiments, until a freak nuclear explosion bonded them to him.

2 He was misdiagnosed with brain damage after the accident, but it was actually his mind adjusting so he could mentally control the tentacles.

3 His brilliant scientific mind has made Doc Ock a criminal genius, and the original leader of the Sinister Six.

DOC OCK'S BRILLIANT MIND AND FOUR MECHANICAL LIMBS BRING A WHOLE NEW MEANING TO THE PHRASE ARMED AND DANGEROUS! READ ON TO FIND OUT EIGHT FACTS ABOUT THIS TENTACLED TERROR!

FIRST APPEARANCE

Amazing Spider-Man #3 (1963)

4 Doc Ock's mental control of his tentacles is so strong, he can manipulate them from 500 miles away.

5 Each tentacle can strike with the force of a jackhammer, and lift objects weighing up to 20 tons!

6 He can use his tentacles to climb sheer walls, travel high above the ground, and even move at 50 miles per hour.

7 When battling loads of opponents, Doc Ock can control his tentacles so precisely that each one can fight a different person simultaneously!

8 In his very first battle with Spider-Man, Doc Ock gave him such a hiding, the wall-crawler considered hanging up his web-shooters for good!

ANSWERS

04 CRIMINAL CONNECTIONS

CRIMINAL CONNECTIONS:

PICTURE IMPERFECT:
A=Captain America, B=Rhino,
C=Silver Surfer, D=Sandman.

16 SPIDEY CENTRAL!

CRACK THE CODE: 8, 6, 9, 1, 8
HAVING A BLAST: B
SMOKE SCREEN:
A-WAR MACHINE;
B-IRON MONGER;
C-MELTER; D-IRON MAN

31 EYE SPIDEY

31 SPIDEY CENTRAL

RESCUE MISSION: B

52 SPIDEY CENTRAL

ALL TIED UP: B
DEADLY DISGUISE: D
WICKED WORDS: 7